Arm Up, Rookie!

Written & Illustrated by Sarah Schaff

Dedication:

To Skylie Eden, Mazie Mo, and Rookie Wayne, may you always remember to "Arm Up!"

Acknowledgements:

First off, I would like to thank my Jesus, who placed yet another story on my heart. Second, I want to thank my family who has encouraged me in pursuing my writing journey. Especially my husband and son who were my inspirations for this book. Third, I would like to thank my book designer, Christy Martinez, who has been gifted with so many talents, but her friendship and natural creativity is what I appreciate the most. Fourth, I would like to thank my writer's group who continues to push me to grow.

Layout and design by Christy Martinez
www.madeprettyagain.com

"I ain't scared of nothin...well except for the dark, and Mom's meatloaf, oh, and skunks. They stink something awful, and spiders. Even the teeny, tiny ones. Is there a spider on me?! I feel something crawling up my back right now!"

"Are you ready, Rookie?"

"Are you kidding me?! I was born ready! I am ready like a bull busting through the chute gates or a monster truck barreling through the mud bogs!"

"Let's start putting on your gear."

"Oh, I would like to see my sisters try and beat me up wearing this! BAM! KA-POW! HI-YAH!"

"You know, this safety gear reminds me a lot of the 'Armor of God.' Have you ever heard of the 'Armor of God?'"

"The whaaaaat?"

"The 'Armor of God.' Most of our battles in this life are not of flesh, blood, or even bulls in the arena. That means they are not with actual people or animals, but they are unseen battles that take place in our hearts and minds. The enemy, who is the devil, is the cause of all unseen battles. He wants nothing more than to cause confusion in our faith in God. He wants us to hate other people and to think we are better than others, which is called pride. The enemy's goal is to lead us away from Jesus. But, just like the safety gear protects our body from the bull, the 'Armor of God' protects our hearts and minds from the devil's unseen attacks."

"Rookie, whether you earn a belt buckle in the arena today or not, you must always put on the belt of truth. The truth is God loves you, died for you and created you with purpose. Not only do you need to know that truth, you need to speak truth as well. Speaking lies opens up a door for the enemy to come into your life, and you don't want that, Son."

"Ummm...Dad, the other day I took candy out of the candy jar when Mom wasn't looking... and when I say candy, I mean a lot. I felt sick and told Mom that it was a stomach bug, but I lied. I don't think I can eat candy ever again!"

"Thank you for telling me the truth, Son. Now go tell Mom."

"Oh, man."

"The protective vest that you put on is like the 'Breast Plate of Righteousness.' Righteousness means perfect or without blame. The only one who is perfect is God, but He made us right by sending us His Son, Jesus, to die on the cross for our sins. Just like your vest protects your vital organs like your heart and lungs, God's righteousness protects your heart forever."

"You mean you are not perfect, Dad?"

"Far from it, Son, and neither are you. Hence the candy jar."

"Your cowboy boots represent your feet being fitted with the 'Gospel of Peace.' When we realize that God loves us and made us right with Him, even in the middle of our mistakes, like the candy jar, it gives us peace. So, we need to put on our boots and share the news with others so they can have peace too."

"I think I will start with my Callie girl. She could use some peace. She is one anxious dog."

"Just like the bullfighters protect us from the bulls, 'The Shield of Faith' protects us from the enemy's fiery darts of doubt. Faith is believing in God even though we can't see Him. There is evidence of God all around us, through nature, answered prayers and even peace in our hearts. If you do not have faith that God is with you, then you should not ride today."

"Oh I know that God is with me, I just think God's superpower is invisibility. Can you imagine all the things we could do if we were invisible?!"

"The helmet you have on your head represents the 'Helmet of Salvation.' When you put the helmet on, you are making an eternal choice to choose Jesus and walk with him. Just like the helmet you put on during a rodeo protects your brain, the 'Helmet of Salvation' protects your soul so you can spend eternity with Jesus in Heaven. Eternity means forever and ever. Rookie, have you ever asked Jesus in your heart?"

"Yes, I did! I asked Jesus in my heart on September 22, 2019, while lying in bed with Mom."

"I am proud of you, Rookie. That is the best decision you will ever make."

"The spurs on your boots allow you to fight back with the beast you are riding much like the 'Sword of the Spirit.' The 'Sword of the Spirit' is the Bible. If you want to hear God's voice, the Bible is most often where He speaks to us. The Bible gives us wisdom, allows us to hear God's heart and gives us strength to stand up to the enemy's attacks."

"Wow! That is real superhero stuff right there, huh, Dad? When we get home tonight will you read me the Bible? My favorite part is when David cuts off Goliath's head!"

"Of course it is, son. Yes, I will read to you from the Bible."

"Are we ready to ride yet, Dad?"

"Almost, Rookie. After we put on our armor we must always pray."

"Ok Rookie, it is just about time, but before you get on, who are you riding for?"

"You, Dad!"

"No, Son. We ride for the One who protects us and is with us, Jesus. Always remember, 'Be strong and courageous! Do not be afraid; do not be discouraged. The Lord your God is with you wherever you go.' And that includes this dusty old arena."

"Now, arm up, Rookie, and let's ride!"

Rookie and his Callie girl

Bible Verse References

"Finally, be strong in the Lord and in his mighty power. Put on the full armor of God so that you can take your stand against the devil's schemes. For our struggles are not against flesh and blood, but against the rulers, against the authorities, against the powers of the dark world and against the spiritual forces of evil in the heavenly realms. Therefore put on the full armor of God, so that when the day of evil comes, you may be able to stand your ground, and after you have done everything, to stand. Stand firm then, with the belt of truth buckled around your waist, with the breast plate of righteousness in place, and with your feet fitted with the readiness that comes from the gospel of peace. In addition to all this, take up the shield of faith, with which you can extinguish all the flaming arrows of the evil one. Take the helmet of salvation and the sword of the spirit, which is the word of God. And pray in the spirit on all occasions with all kinds of prayers and requests. With this in mind, be alert and always keep praying for all of the saints."

Ephesians 6:10-18 (NIV)

"Have I not commanded you? Be strong and courageous. Do not be terrified; do not be discouraged, for the Lord your God will be with you wherever you go."

Joshua 1:9 (NIV)

Rookie and his daddy,
2019 Casper Fair & Rodeo
Mutton Busting

Rookie's Daddy, 2002

About the Author

Sarah is a lover of Jesus and is blessed to be a stay at home mom. She was raised in Boise, ID, but has spent the last 16 years in Casper, WY with her husband and three children. God has given her a love for painting, drawing, and writing and He uses creativity to connect to her heart. Sarah feels very much inspired by her children and challenges herself to see the world through their eyes. After all, we are all called to have "faith like a child." She feels that God has definitely placed each story on her heart with a special message to share. When Sarah is not being creative you will probably find her and her family spending time with their furry and feathered friends consisting of dogs, cats, chickens, ducks, a fluffy bunny, and a pigeon that literally wears pants. Much of the characters in her stories were inspired by her very own menagerie. Sarah's other faith-based children's books are: "A Brave Knight's Quest," "Tazie and her Two-nicorn the-not-so Unicorn," "When Heaven's Gates Sprung Open Wide," "Arm Up, Rookie!" and "Just Keep Purring, Keep Purring with Purpose" with many more to come. All of Sarah's books are available on Amazon and Etsy. Also check out "Acrylics 139" Etsy shop for more scripture doodle encouragements including: coloring books, greeting cards, magnets, bookmarks, and stickers.

www.etsy.com/shop/acrylics139

CPSIA information can be obtained
at www.ICGtesting.com
Printed in the USA
BVHW020713050521
605599BV00012B/20